# KEEPING A
# DUCKS
# IN YOUR GARDEN

**A Kitchen Garden Book**

By the same Author
In the same series
Goose on the Green
Keeping a Few Hens in Your Garden
Food from the Kitchen Garden
Beekeeping for Beginners (by Penelope Hands)
A Peacock on the Lawn (with S. Carpenter)
A Henkeepers' Journal
The Big Book of Garden Hens

A Christmas Journal

Published by the Kitchen Garden 2002
Church Cottage Troston
Bury St Edmunds Suffolk IP31 1EX
Tel 01359 268 322
Email: francine@jfraymond.demon.co.uk
www.kitchen-garden-hens.co.uk

ISBN 0-9532857-5-8

With thanks to the Greys

From F W Harvey's poem-Ducks
*'From troubles of the world*
*I turn to ducks*
*Beautiful comical things'.*

## Introduction

Ducks have the best of all worlds. They can walk - albeit gracelessly - and swim and fly. Endlessly entertaining to watch in any of these elements, many of us will have fed them from pushchairs during visits to village ponds and parks. I bet the word 'duck' features high on the list of babies' first words.

With these memories in mind, ten years ago we excavated a pond. Planting up the banks with indigenous wildflowers, we built a pontoon so our sons could lie on their tummies and watch the wildlife that soon took up residence. Later we were entranced as a wild Mallard duck and her eleven ducklings made their home among the lily pads. We watched them grow (like wildfire) and then disappear in autumn to join the flock on the village duck pond. Imagine our horror as the following spring those eleven fat Mallard re-appeared - with mates, and had similar success raising their offspring. You can guess the rest. Within a couple of years our garden was awash with ducks who turned our beautiful pond into a duckpond.

We struggled to feed them and witnessed their lurid love lives. We raced out, arms akimbo to rescue put-upon females courted by dozens of sex-mad Lotharios. Every morning we woke bleary-eyed to their raucous dawn chorus, raised their orphans and developed a love-hate relationship with the flock, but a continuing love affair with individual birds. Ducks are huge time-wasters and their antics a source of great amusement.

Then one day I went to visit my friend John Grey and realized that it was possible to keep a *controllable* flock of ducks in a smallish garden, and tasted delicious fresh duck eggs for the first time. Sadly this is probably not a system I'll ever be able to practise here. We seem to be imprinted in the local wild duck population's consciousness as an easy lay. But mindful of my love for ducks, I offer this painless system to keep just a *few* ducks in your garden.

I suggest you buy a couple of ducks and a drake and keep them in a duckhouse inside a run, with a pond and as much access to your garden as you can bear. Ducks are very messy and you must be prepared to clean up regularly, devote ten minutes a day to their welfare and as much space as you can spare. This apart, you need just a little common sense and to stick to a few basic principles. I hope what follows will de-mystify the situation.

## Where to Begin

In most areas you don't need permission to keep poultry in your garden, but check with the Environmental Health Department at your local Town Hall. Next, consult your neighbours to see if they'll help with your flock while you're on holiday and are prepared to put up with the odd quack. If everyone's happy, then decide where to site your run and pond. Choose a spot that offers shade and shelter from the wind, as spacious and secure as possible. As with all poultry, your birds' main enemies are uncontrolled dogs, especially terriers and of course, foxes. If you live in a really foxy area it's not worth the heartbreak - or the expense.

On to expense. Assuming you decide on a couple of ducks, you can expect to pay little more than a few pounds a month on feed, depending on how free range your birds are and how much surplus rice, pasta, and bread your household produces. Pure breeds are more expensive to buy than other poultry, especially the ornamentals, so stick to less exotic breeds to start with. Your duck house can cost as much or as little as you want, but I suggest you buy one large enough for you to feed them in, plus room for a nest box, or you can adapt an existing garden shed.

Choosing your ducks will be fun. As with hens, most pure breeds were developed originally for the table or to produce endless eggs. Then the showmen got hold of them and exaggerated their physical idiosyncrasies. Try to find utility strains - not highly-bred show birds, unless you are prepared to give them five star treatment. Go to local poultry shows and scan the smallholders' magazines. The Domestic Waterfowl Club will provide lists of breeders (see Directory page at the back of this book). Always visit before buying and give yourself plenty of time to order. You may have to wait for eggs to hatch and ducklings to grow.

Adopt a routine, like the one John Grey has developed. His Khaki Campbells are fed in the morning inside their shed and left until they lay - usually by 9am and the eggs are collected daily to be eaten fresh. His flock of four are then let out into the garden with a small pond and they potter around until sunset when supper is served in their quarters and they are shut up for the night. On long summer evenings they sometimes want to linger, so John herds them in with long sticks.

Finally, although ducks are hardy and easy to keep, remember they must be visited morning and evening and cleaned out regularly because they are *very* messy. It won't take long, but beware - keeping ducks can develop into a consuming passion.

## Where to Keep Your Ducks

Many old books promote breeds of ducks able to exist without water. Those destined for the table would have been prevented from swimming for fear of losing weight, but no-one who has seen how ducks take to water would be able to deny them a pond - a paddling pool at the very least. They seem happy, even in the most appalling conditions, but please give them as much water as possible, they love to wallow - and don't overcrowd. But remember, even a shallow pond can be dangerous to small children, so make sure the whole area is securely fenced off.

The ideal duck home is a shed in a netted area with a pond and a gate leading to occasional access to your garden - depending on their security and how fussy a gardener you are. Keep them in a covered area for the first two weeks until they know their address. The smaller breeds (and Muscovies who fly surprisingly well despite their size) may need the flight feathers on one wing trimmed (see p.29) but ask your breeder to do this. Subsequent generations won't need curtailing. If you have a river, wire net an area right down to the riverbed, but visiting wild duck will always be a problem.

Ducks are very hardy. House them for protection from predators and easy egg collection, rather than nighttime comfort. They'll need 2sq ft/60sq cm per bird with above head-height ventilation, though high space is wasted (unless you want to get in there as well) because ducks don't perch like hens. An ordinary 8' x 4' /2.40m x1.20m garden shed would be fine for 8 ducks. The floor should be kept dry, with newspaper, straw or dried leaves, but needs regular washing down with a hose, so a concrete flag floor with a drain would be best.

Your house must be foxproof with a proper door, have a 6 ft/1.80m high wire run with a roof and the bottom 6"/15cm dug into the ground as an extra deterrent. Cut away any overhanging branches from surrounding trees. A determined fox will visit every day until you make a mistake and leave the door open. Perhaps you should shelve your duck keeping plans for another time or place if you know there are foxes about.

If you are building a concrete pond, it should be about a foot deep, and able to be cleaned with a broom and hose. A simple shaped fibreglass garden pond is easy to clean by running a hose to overflow. Nowadays a water feature in the garden is obligatory, but ducks and lily ponds are not compatible. Plant hardy, rampant greenery, but keep their roots in sacking and cover with heavy flints to stop ducks dabbling them away.

A large pond with an island in the middle may seem ideal, but don't forget foxes swim and can walk on ice, if not on water (and you're unlikely to want to when inspection is essential). If you are excavating a pond, use a liner - butyl is the strongest, but fold strong green plastic mesh round the turf perimeter of your pond to stop your ducks eating the edges away. Alternatively, protect banks with flints, large logs or flagstones with a camber so splashes flow back in again. Deep gravel tends to disappear over time. Your pond will silt up and need topping up during droughts.

The Domestic Fowl Trust supplies a mail order duck pond and will send out an excellent catalogue (see Directory). You could use a child's paddling pool with rigid sides as an extra temporary pond for big ducklings with a ramp to get in and out, but not an inflatable - they have quite sharp claws. Ducks need shade and can suffer from sunstroke so put up bamboo screens, but in an average garden this should not be a problem. Offer shelter in the winter with strategically placed straw bales.

## Which Breed

All domestic ducks are developed from wild Mallard - familiar to us all on ponds and parks and tamed throughout history. Pure black and white ducks occur naturally as sports, the latter bred and eaten for their paler flesh. Pools and moats on country estates relied on wild fowl as well as fish for food, using nets, falcons and shooting to catch their prey. Historic reports of medieval kitchen gardens prefer to concentrate on doves - a courtlier example of enduring love than the Mallard *rampant.* Cottagers would have kept ducks for food and wild duck are still raised in pens for wildfowlers' sport.

Breeds were developed for their laying potential - Khaki Campbells can lay almost an egg a day - more than hens. Heavy birds like the Aylesbury and the Rouen were obviously destined for the table. The more decorative ducks were bred as ornamentals and decoy ducks were bred for sport. Muscovies are a separate species, probably more closely related to geese.

My rainbow tribe is made up of escapees from a local game farm interbred somewhere with Campbells, Call Ducks and Whites. Unforgivable as far as the purists are concerned, they are prodigiously willing and able to reproduce and like most natural hybrids - their vigour is legendary.

Starting from scratch, I would buy a mature pure breed trio - a drake and 2 ducks and then hatch out some ducklings in the following years, bringing my flock up to numbers my garden and pond could cope with, (far, far fewer than I can see from my window now). A small garden will be fine with just two ducks. Unlike cockerels, drakes get on quite well together although they bicker a bit in the mating season, but don't have too many or your ducks will be pestered. Both can live for about 10 years. In some breeds the duck and drake are similar - the male just a little bigger with a couple of curled tail feathers; in others, with Mallard in their make-up, the sexes look totally different. Only ducks quack, drakes have a *basso* rasping croak.

If you have a small garden and little appetite for eggs (or *duck à l'orange*) I can recommend the bantam breeds or tiny Call Ducks, known in Holland as *Kwackers.* They come in lots of different colours. Their only drawback is a really irritating quack, which can start at 4am in the morning.

Here we highlight our favourite 8 breeds, but coming a close second, the Orpington perfected in 1900 by William Cook who bred my beloved Buff Orpington hens; the Cayuga - a large shiny black duck and the Blue Swedish in stylish slate grey and black with a white bib.

**Aylesbury** (UK) 10lbs/4.10kg.
Pure white - with a pinkish-white bill, orange legs and webs (aka feet) perfected over the centuries as a table duck *par excellence* by small breeders in Buckinghamshire. Deep keeled with a low slung undercarriage in show birds - avoid extremes. Lays about 100 white eggs a year and will breed if not too fat.

**Black East Indian** (South America) 2lbs/800g.
Ornamental, tiny, with a lustrous beetle green sheen, smart matching black legs and webs. Able to find food in the garden, relishes insects and slugs. Will breed and fly - wing feathers need clipping (see p.29). Similar to, but smaller than the Cayuga. Probably originally a black Mallard sport.

**Call Duck** (UK) Under 2lbs/800g.
Dear little things - firm and cobby with a nice round head. Constant, rather irritating quack used as a decoy to lure Mallard at shoots. Various colours: White, Blue, Buff, Magpie, Silver, Apricot, Mallard and Pied. They eat grass and cause little damage in the garden.

**Campbell** (Gloucestershire - UK) 5lbs/2.05kg.
Bred by a Mrs Campbell from Indian Runners, Rouen and Mallard in 1900 for eggs. Pretty birds with sloping carriage, not upright like Runners. Slim and active. 1 drake to 6 ducks. Prolific Khaki, also in White and Dark. John Grey's favourite.

**Indian Runner** (India) 4-5lbs/2kg.
Brought to England from the East by a Scots sea captain via Dumfries and Cumbria in 1850. The other premier egg layer. Eggs white, same size as hen's egg. Will forage. Upright consort's stance with hands behind back. Also in Fawn/white, Fawn, Black, White and Chocolate. Appealing and curious.

**Muscovy** (S.America) Drake 12lbs/5.50kg Duck 6lbs/2.75kg.
Drake has no curved tail but is much bigger and has a strange knob on his head. Can be pugnacious to other drakes. The ducks don't quack. Will cross with other breeds but their offspring will be sterile. Good parents and broodies. 7 varieties. A feature in times past, of Derry and Toms' roof garden in Kensington.

**Pekin** (China) white eggs 8lbs/3.60kg.
Creamy white to canary yellow with a yellow bill, but slimmer and more upstanding than the Aylesbury - good layers, developed in 1870. Friendly, inquisitive birds with soft eyes.

**Rouen** (France) 10lbs/4.10kg
Bruiser of the duck world, looks like a very fat Mallard. Largest duck, bred unsurprisingly for the table in France. Has majestic bulk, but should not be overweight, allow plenty of opportunity for exercise as can be lazy. Greenish eggs.

## What to feed your ducks

Basically ducks need water, grit, grass and food. Like hens, they are omnivores, and left to their own devices with the run of a large garden will balance their own nutritional requirements with just a little help from you. They need a diet of grain (in the form of mixed corn) and a little protein, bought as pellets. Don't give them mash, because ducks turn everything into mash. These fundamentals are naturally supplemented with insects and worms, (and you hope slugs and snails) from the garden, green stuff from the kitchen and grass from their surroundings.

Offer corn in a hopper for 20 minutes twice a day, when you get up and again at sunset, and leave them to supplement it with natural food. If you are keeping ducks for lots of eggs, feed 80% mixed corn to 20% poultry pellets from your feed merchant (look him up in Yellow Pages). Allen and Page and Marriages (see Directory) are the best poultry feed brands. If ducks are kept entirely in a run, the ground must be divided in two or four sections and rested frequently, otherwise the area will get very mucky indeed, especially around the pond.

Galvanized Eltex feeders, hoppers and drinkers are hardier and nicer looking than plastic alternatives, except in freezing weather when several plastic washing up bowls are best. Water is absolutely essential - even one day without can be fatal to ducks. Grit is available naturally in your garden, but remember to buy and supply if for any reason your ducks are confined to a pen. The maize in mixed corn will bring out the clotted cream colour in Pekins and enhance orange legs, beaks and webs.

My army also love barley (available in mixed corn), boiled rice, brown bread soaked in water, pasta, sweetcorn kernels, peanuts, and old cheese. Their bills enable them to pick up food quite delicately, or to dabble and sieve food by sucking in water. I have ducks who situate themselves permanently and hopefully under bird tables. Perhaps that's how the upright stance of the Runner and Pekin first developed. They'll eat weeds, seeds, leaves, grass clippings, brassica leaves and squashed snails. I've never actually seen a duck eat a slug, but I'm assured they do.

John Grey says his Campbells love fruit peel and pips (not citrus), and my ducks always finish off the windfall apples, especially once they have started to ferment. I swear I see them swagger more than usual. Keep your grain and pellets in separate galvanized dustbins with metal lids to deter vermin and make sure that leftover food is always put away between feeds.

# Eggs

Duck eggs have always been unpopular. Somewhere in the general consciousness (probably as a result of some World War II Ministry of Food edict) lurks the idea that duck eggs are likely to have salmonella. Because the shells are more porous than those of hens, bacteria can pass easily into the egg, especially if ducks are kept in horrid conditions. But with scrupulous hygiene and prompt collection, as with my friends the Greys, your duck eggs, like their Campbells' eggs should be safe and tasty.

Eat them fresh. Most ducks lay before 9am, so collect and clean immediately, dry cleaning if possible, or wash in warm water and dry. Discard any eggs that you find in the run or laid in the garden or pond. Don't leave them lying around, even though they are very pretty, or they'll attract rats, crows and other vermin, and encourage your ducks to go broody and lay away.

Build a couple of nest boxes 12" x 12"/30cm x 30cm (or made to measure for larger birds), line with straw and place in the darker recesses of the duckhouse. Change the straw regularly to prevent the eggs getting soiled.

White ducks lay white eggs, and so do Runners. Rouens lay pale green and Cayugas lay cream to dark green eggs. They are great for cooking - especially baking, and good mixed with hens' eggs for omelettes and scrambled eggs. Eat them fresh, before they are a week old because they have a shorter shelf life than hens' eggs. I have eaten them boiled at the Grey's house, straight from the nestbox and would have been hard pushed to tell them from hens' eggs. Ducks lay well for three years and then gradually lay less. You don't need a drake for eggs, only for fertile ones.

After you've been keeping ducks for a while, and assuming you have a drake, you may decide, come Spring to augment your flock by hatching and rearing a few ducklings from eggs. If you want to try a new breed or don't have a drake, you can buy fertile eggs of any variety from breeders to hatch at home. Do remember though the extra mess that comes with extra ducks.

Duck eggs take 28 days to hatch (Muscovies 34-36). Only set eggs that are less than 7 days old. Collect them daily, date mark with a soft pencil and keep them in a cool place (59F/15C). Turn daily, first to the left, the next day to the right. Reject any that are damaged, oddly shaped or unusually big or small.

Duck eggs are traditionally hatched under broody hens (see Keeping a Few Hens in your Garden) and they can of course be incubated (see Domesticated Ducks and Geese by Joseph Batty).

Generally though, I feel they should be hatched and reared as naturally as possible. A good mum can pass on a huge amount of important information. Their maternal behaviour has a bad reputation, but it depends on the bird, not on the breed. Some like Rouens and Muscovies usually make good hatchers, though the breeds that lay best paradoxically make the worst sitters.

Ducklings grow at a spectacular rate, much faster than chicks and a hen foster mum will be horrified at the early independence and aquatic proclivities of her charges. Mature at 4 months, young ducks can lay their first eggs in September - but I find they don't sit or raise babes well until their second or third year. Some never manage, scattering their young to perish as they hare round the village.

## Augmenting your Flock

Ducks are gregarious birds and introducing newcomers is easy. Just make sure they are kept under cover for two weeks until they get used to their new home. Young birds without a mum to support them will have to be segregated until they can hold their own, but hatching out your own ducklings is the most natural way to increase your stock. Please remember that keeping too many ducks in your garden will result in chaos, so do as I say, not as I do.

Drakes should be kept with ducks for at least 4 weeks to be sure eggs will be fertile. Increase the percentage of layers pellets to grain for the ladies, but drakes need little encouragement to mate. They are legendarily promiscuous, indulging in elaborate display behaviour. They say water is essential for successful lovemaking. My Lotharios will mate anywhere, especially in groups. They are the gang bangers of the avian world.

They start to pair in January, bickering endlessly and the ducks go broody as the weather warms up. One drake can cope with 4-8 ducks, though in the wild it's often the other way round and the poor females have a really bad time. All ducks will crossbreed and often your pure breed duck will fall for some free-flying Romeo wild Mallard and subsequent ducklings may not favour their pure breed father.

Place a couple of large broody eggs in the nestbox to encourage your duck to lay in her house. When she is sitting, introduce the eggs you have been storing or leave her to lay her clutch.

Remember, not too many. She will line the nest with soft down plucked from her breast, covering her eggs when she nips out to feed. If she has laid away and is sitting on a clutch in the garden, she will be prone to predators, hence the term sitting duck. If tame, you may be able to move her plus nest and a few of the eggs, but she'll probably abandon them.

Make sure she has food and enough water in the run to immerse and preen her head and that any mess is cleared daily, especially from the nest. The incubation period is 28 days from the time she starts sitting and when the ducklings hatch they will stay under their mum for two days, surviving on food from the egg. After two days, she will lead them out - reward her with a big feed. Remove any unhatched eggs.

Unlike most birds, parent ducks don't feed their young, except by example. Once they have hatched, keep them in a covered run (see p. 25) with a partially boarded top, in a sheltered spot. This run can also be used as a hospital wing. The mother will call her babes over to feed from a terracotta flowerpot saucer with chick crumbs and to drink from a chick drinker. Don't let them near any open water for the first few days, or they'll jump in and chill. My ducks take their babes to the pond, safe from predators on day one, but there is a high mortality rate. Move the cage every day to keep the grass fresh. You can open it at the end of the first week (but close at night) and let them out into the run and then finally into the garden.

Clean the water every day in gradually bigger containers, but nothing too deep sided or the little ones will be unable to get out. Give your ducklings *ad lib* chick or turkey crumbs for the first two weeks, and then grower pellets and wet mixed corn. Ducklings can be sexed by late summer by their quack or croak.

I have raised abandoned ducklings with success. I'm not sure I should recommend it, but pairs do well. Keep them in a box, warm in an old sweater under an anglepoise lamp. Feed every hour on a little mashed hardboiled egg mixed with moist brown bread and a drop of codliver oil. Supply with a turf to dabble; let them swim in the sink and cuddle in the crook of your neck, but encourage them to join flock asap. Nowadays sadly, I harden my heart even though there is probably nothing more appealing than a tiny duckling - I'm afraid it's just too time consuming. I always had something down my jumper and found myself turning down social engagements because of my charges.

## Gardening with ducks

I must admit that ducks would not be my first choice as co-gardeners. But if you are going to keep them, it is essential for both ducks and the spot of land you earmark for them, that you allow as much space as you possibly can. Ideally, access to a paddock, orchard, wood or piece of wild garden would be the best habitat. But if your entire garden is under cultivation, perhaps you can give them limited access for a couple of hours a day, or maybe during the autumn and winter months.

The two main problems (the downside of ducks) are the trample factor - ducks have big feet - and the mess, especially round the pond. Lawns can be cleaned with a besom or a quick burst of a highspeed hose. Vulnerable areas can be protected with a variety of low wire fences and cloches. I find mine eat the compost in my raised beds and virtually anything that is green and sappy will be nibbled or trampled to the ground. Be warned.

Say goodbye to frogs, frogspawn and any other pond wildlife. You could keep an extra pond, with weld mesh wire panels over it, so the wild life can creep through and plants poke out. Keep your duckpond ice free in winter with a small electric heater, like those used by fish fanciers.

On the upside, your ducks will eat many garden pests. Their droppings will fertilize the garden soil and their old bedding will make excellent compost when added to the heap in layers with other garden waste. John Grey assures me that on the whole, his Campbells do more good than harm in his garden.

Ducks get on well with other garden familiars. They mix with hens, ignoring each other, unless there are babies or get too greedy at mealtimes. Ducks are bullied by geese, so give them plenty of space. Your own cats and dogs can be trained (mine have never transgressed) but other people's pets can be a problem especially with ducklings. Make sure their run is secure. Foxes are the worst, but I've had awful experiences with a heron who would spear a duckling and fly away, followed by a distraught mum. Their noise would wake me and I'd race out. Finally he gave up and rustled some fish fancier's pond instead.

Keeping ducks encourages other birds to your garden. Duck feathers will soon line all their nests. (Some like crows and pigeons should be discouraged). I love to see the swallows gathering mud from the pond and swooping down to catch the midges. Sadly, duck eggs and ducklings will also prove tempting to magpies, crows, jays and sparrow hawks, as well as mink, squirrels, rats and stoats, which is why unprotected in the wild, Mallard have such huge families.

## Problems

Ducks seem to be amazingly hardy creatures - mine thrive with very little input from me. Allow them plenty of space with as much access to your garden as you can bear. If they are kept on the same bit of land for too long they will catch worms. Your vet can supply a remedy. Provide lots of clean water for drinking and bathing, or your ducks will get sore eye ducts. Ducks kept on the hard with no swimming facilities can develop corns and calluses on their feet. Just occasionally one of mine lands badly and limps for a while, or a duck will be pestered by too many drakes, so I isolate the patient in the run or the hospital wing.

Ducks moult in September to November and your garden will be full of feathers. Smaller ornamental ducks and bantams or Muscovies may need one wing clipped to stop them straying. Get your breeder to do it and watch. By the time the feathers have grown your birds will have settled and future generations won't need it. Never trim feathers during the moult.

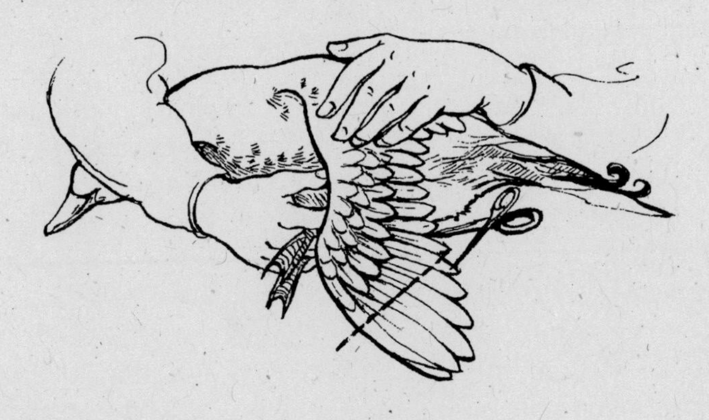

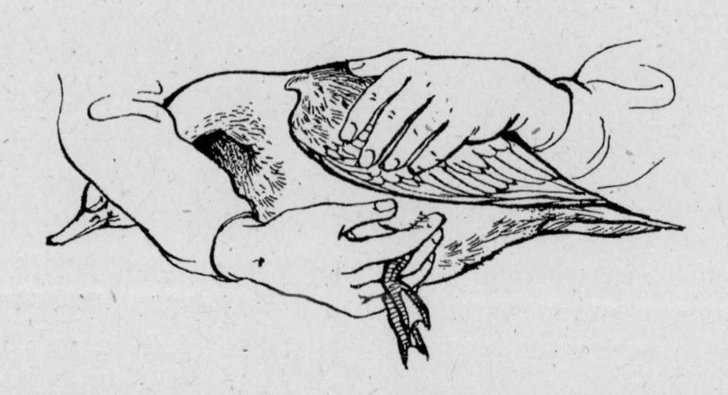

Like hens, ducks can develop breathing problems from damp bedding. Make sure yours sleep on straw - not hay which harbours fungal bacteria, and clean your house regularly with Virkon disinfectant. Wounds should be treated with gentian violet antiseptic spray (from your vet). Isolate the patient in the hospital run.

Make sure that your birds have access to shade because sunstroke is not uncommon, especially if their water supply dries up as well. Isolate with plenty of both if you notice a duck sitting with laboured breathing.

Like hens, ducks are very difficult to catch. They always seem to know what you have in mind. I trap mine by building a cage, feeding them ever nearer and then inside it. Then I drop the door, but this takes about a week. You can catch them in their house at night, but if you need them immediately use an angler's fish-landing net. I've had occasional success with a large bamboo cloche, but have been considered a murderer by the entire flock for at least a fortnight afterwards.
Move slowly among your ducks, preferably wearing the same

clothes. I've been greeted with complete horror, just because I was wearing a hat - and I thought it suited me. Ducks are generally inquisitive and friendly creatures, but are suspicious of things that move, like wheelbarrows and hosepipes.

If you have to handle a bird, slide one hand under the tummy and hold the legs, keeping the neck under your arm (see opposite). Watch out for sharp claws especially on Muscovies. If you need to transport ducks, place them in a strong, ventilated cardboard box, lined with lots of newspaper, and place on the back seat of the car, rather than in an airless boot.

Rats are the poultry keeper's number one enemy. Deter by keeping your feed in bins and make sure food is put away at night. Your house should be strong and built on legs, so rats can't lurk underneath, safe from cats or terriers, or built on concrete, so rats can't tunnel inside. Vermin will also take eggs, so collect every day and keep ducklings caged. There is an ingenious device called the Wide Piper (see Directory) that dispenses poison without endangering other creatures.

Ducks and Geese at Home by Michael and Victoria Roberts (see Directory) goes into thorough and gruesome detail on the subject of killing, plucking and drawing for those who can make the leap from garden pets to *Magret de Canard.* If you have to cull a bird because of injury or illness, I would always take them to the vet. Hopefully though your ducks will live long and pleasant stress-free lives, giving you and your family lots of pleasure, a consuming passion and a supply of delicious eggs.

**Directory**

| | |
|---|---|
| Eltex - feeders and drinkers - for stockists | 01384 566 838 |
| Wide Piper - rat poison dispenser | 01514 207 151 |
| Marriages - for feed - for stockists | 01245 612 000 |
| Allen and Page - for feed - for stockists | 01362 822 900 |
| The Domestic Fowl Trust - good catalogue | 01386 833 083 |

Domesticated Ducks and Geese - Dr Batty - Beech Publications
Small Scale Poultry Keeping - Faber
Ducks & Geese at Home - M & V Roberts - Golden Cockerel
Domestic Ducks and Geese - Fred Hams - Shire Publications
Rock & Water Gardening - Peter Robinson - Lorenz
Keeping a Few Hens in Your Garden - Francine Raymond

| | |
|---|---|
| The Domestic Wildfowl Club | 01488 638 014 |
| The British Call Duck Club | 01545 580 425 |

The Kitchen Garden Shop at Church Lane in Troston, near Bury St Edmunds in Suffolk is open from Easter Saturday till the end of September 10 till 5. Please phone first to make sure. 01359 268 322 (All our books are available by mail order from this number). Or visit our website www.kitchen-garden-hens.co.uk

For poultry information visit www.henkeepersassociation.co.uk